HEATHCLIFF
SMOOTH SAILING

The funniest feline in America delights millions of fans every day as he appears in over 500 news-papers. You'll have a laugh a minute as Heathcliff tangles with the milkman, the cat show judge, the veterinarian and just about everyone else he runs into. If you're looking for some fun, look no fur-ther — Heathcliff is here!

HEATHCLIFF®
SMOOTH SAILING

by

Geo Gately

CHARTER BOOKS, NEW YORK

Cartoons previously published in
Heathcliff In Concert

HEATHCLIFF SMOOTH SAILING

A Charter Book / published by arrangement with
McNaught Syndicate, Inc.

PRINTING HISTORY
Special Charter Book Club edition / January 1987

Charter Books are published by The Berkley Publishing Group,
200 Madison Avenue, New York, New York 10016.
PRINTED IN THE UNITED STATES OF AMERICA

"THE MILK AND COOKIES WILL BE ENOUGH FOR SANTA CLAUS!"

"EEYAH!"

"...OH, IT'S THE JANITOR."

"HIS FRIEND ISN'T AMUSED."

"YOU DID IT !... WHY SHOULD I GET INVOLVED ?!"

"COO, COO !... COO, COO!... COO, COO !"

"DOESN'T THIS HURRICANE SEASON EVER END?!"

"NOT 'HURRICANE HEATHCLIFF'!"

" ....AT THIS POINT, THE SAUCER ENCOUNTERED A SMART ALEC...."

"WHAT SAY WE *SHARE* THE AIR CONDITIONER ?!"

"HE'S SCALPING TICKETS TO HIS OWN CONCERT!"

"HAH! I GOT HIM GOOD!"

"BUT HE GOT MY DENTURES."

"IT SAYS 'YOU BETTER STOP DUMPING THOSE GARBAGE CANS'!"

"WILL THE OWNER OF A 1980 RED KITTY SPORT CAR, LICENSE NUMBER 'MEW 123', PLEASE REPORT TO THE PARKING LOT?"

"EXPECTING A VISIT FROM THE LAW ?!!"

" I CAN NOT BE HELD RESPONSIBLE FOR
THE QUALITY OF THE PROGRAMS. "

"I GUESS HE WASN'T HUNGRY."

"JUST TAKE THE PRESCRIPTION TO YOUR
PHARMACIST, IF YOU DON'T MIND!"

"WOULD YOU BUY A USED CAR FROM THAT CAT ?"

"HE CAN SEE THAT I CAME BACK
WITH AN EMPTY TRUCK!"

"HE HATES THE MASKED MARVEL!"

"THERE'S YOUR TROUBLE."

" HE'S ALLERGIC TO SECOND PLACE."

"BARNEY'S HAD A LITTLE TOO MUCH TO DRINK!"

"THE JURY WILL DISREGARD THAT LAST OUTBURST!"

"HIS PREVIOUS RECORD IS FIVE!"

"I THOUGHT THIS WAS OUR BRIDGE NIGHT!"

"NO, NO, HEATHCLIFF!...DON'T DO IT!!"

"LOOKS LIKE YOU WON'T GET TO THE 'FATHER AND SON' DINNER TONIGHT!"

"THANKS FOR COMING BY!"

"RELAX...HE FIXED THE FURNACE."

"NO WONDER HE WON'T EAT!...THAT'S NOT HIS *THURSDAY BOWL!*"

"I DON'T NEED YOUR COMPLETE HISTORY."

"I DON'T LIKE IT!"

"HE'S RAISING PIGEONS!"

"THEY'RE BITING ON CUCKOOS!"

"HE DIDN'T EVEN DUMP IT!... ALL HE TOOK
WAS A BANANA PEEL."

"I CAN'T FIND MY SKI MASK."

"GET OFF MY RECLINER!"

" IT'S TIME FOR TURKEY LEFTOVERS...

...SO, HE'S GOT HIMSELF A BIRD DOG!"

"BIG WEEKEND ?!"

"YOU WERE SAYING...."

"YOU'RE RIGHT.....IT IS PULLING TO THE LEFT...."

"WE JUST HANDLE THE MONEY,
NOT THE CAT FOOD COUPONS."

"NOWADAYS EVERYONE WEARS BLUE JEANS...
EVEN HEATHCLIFF."

"I SEE HE'S HIRED HIMSELF A GOOD OL' DOWN HOME COUNTRY LAWYER!"

"YOU'VE GOT 'GARBAGE CAN ELBOW'."

"I'M SORRY, FRED.... I SHOULD NEVER HAVE MENTIONED THAT YOU'RE A VETERINARIAN!"

"HE'S ONE OF THE FINEST LEFTHANDERS IN THE GAME TODAY!"

"HE'S GETTING MIXED REVIEWS."

"NEEDED A LITTLE CREAM FOR YOUR COFFEE?"

"DON'T LET HIM INTIMIDATE YOU."

"THAT REGISTERED A 7.4 ON THE HEATHCLIFF SCALE!"

"DOES FATSO, HERE, DO ANY TRICKS?"

"WANT YOUR WATCH?"

"WILL YOU STOP CHASING THOSE ANIMALS IN HERE?!"

"I'LL HAVE TO EXAMINE THAT SUITCASE!"

"THIS IS MY LAST PLEA, HEATHCLIFF, OR IT'S 'GOODBYE FOREVER'!"

"THIS TIME I THINK HE'S SERIOUS!"

"NOT EVEN A KISS 'HELLO'?"

"HE'S VERY ACTIVE FOR HIS AGE."

"WHAT WAS THAT BLOOD CURDLING SCREAM
ALL ABOUT ?!"

"HE EATS WHERE THE TRUCK DRIVERS EAT."

"THIS IS THE LAST TIME I ORDER FISH AT A SIDEWALK CAFE!"

"CAN'T BEAT HIM AT SLAPJACK!"

"THEY STOP IN NOW AND THEN FOR A WORKOUT."

"GIFT OR NOT!... YOU CAN'T MAIL THAT!!"

"YOU REALLY GOT HIM ANGRY!"

"HERE'S A BILL FROM THE CHIROPRACTOR...
'ONE BACK SCRATCHED'!"

"I THINK IT'S A SEAFOOD RESTAURANT."

"LET'S TRY 'DIAL-A-PRAYER'!"

"WILL YOU GET HIM OUTA HERE ?!"

"...AND RIGHT ABOUT THERE WOULD BE
THE CAT FOOD AISLE."

"WE WERE OUT FOR OUR MORNING STROLL AND
HE GOT IN THIS TERRIBLE CATFIGHT!"

"NOW, LISTEN TO ME, HEATHCLIFF...
THOSE FISH BELONG TO THE BEAR!"

"HOW'S THE SHRIMP TODAY?"

"MUST BE SOME NEW TV PERSONALITY."

"YOUR SUSPENDERS SHOULD BE HERE IN THIS DRAWER."

"HE'S FILLING A STOCKING FOR A HOMELESS CAT."

"NAW, I DON'T THINK A GIRL WILL EVER BE PRESIDENT...WHAT DO YOU THINK, HEATHCLIFF?"

"NEXT....WAIT YOUR TURN, HEATHCLIFF!"

"AND, WOULD YOU LIKE A FOOTBATH, ALSO?!"

"HEATHCLIFF, YOU'RE AN INCURABLE ROMANTIC!"

"SONJA GAVE HIM A SMOKING JACKET!"

"NEXT TIME, SHE'D BETTER GIVE HIM A PIPE!"

"SOMEONE STUFFED YOUR TROMBONE
INTO THE TACKLING DUMMY!"

"HE'S GOT A GIRL IN EVERY PORT!"

"BOO, HEATHCLIFF!"

"FORGET IT !...WE DON'T NEED IT THAT BAD!"

"WHERE'D YOU GET THE MONEY TO BUY LOBSTER?!"

"EEEEEEEYOWOWOW!!!"

"SORRY, I DON'T DRESS TURKEYS."

"WHAT'S GOING ON HERE, FANG ?!"

"NO ONE ELSE EVER REMEMBERS THE TUNA FLEET!"

"NO THANKS...I'M SICK OF TURKEY SANDWICHES!"

"IT WAS THAT FAT CAT WITH THE STRIPES, AGAIN!"

"HUH?... SHAKE HIM...??"

"AHA!!"

"HE'S REALLY CRACKING DOWN THIS TIME!"

" NEXT. "

"I'LL TEACH HIM HIS TRICKS, THANK YOU!"

"STUFFING?... WHY WOULD I WANT TO EAT STUFFING?!"

"I'LL EDIT THE COMMERCIALS!"

"BEAUTIFUL TIMING, HEATHCLIFF!"

"GOLLY!...IT REALLY IS HEATHCLIFF!... ....IN THE WAX MUSEUM!"

"DON'T ASK!"

"THEY'RE ROASTING DOOLEY, THE DOGCATCHER."

"I THOUGHT YOU MIGHT ENJOY
SOME CRACKERS AND CATNIP DIP."

"SOUP'S ON!"

"IF YOU'RE THIRSTY, THIS WILL HAVE TO DO....
WE'RE FRESH OUT OF BOTTLED SPRING WATER!"

"DINNERTIME, HEATHCLIFF....

...AND TAKE IT EASY....I JUST WAXED THE FLOOR!"

"I THINK THE OLD FOOL HAS GONE CRACKERS!"

"IT'S ONLY A MATTER OF TIME BEFORE
THE RAILROAD COMES THROUGH HERE!"